HEALING WOUNDED HISTORY:

THE WORKBOOK
A Course for Small Groups

RUSS PARKER
and
MICHAEL MITTON

DARTON·LONGMAN + TODD

First published in 2001 by
Darton, Longman and Todd Ltd
1 Spencer Court
140–142 Wandsworth High Street
London SW18 4JJ

ISBN 0-232-52252-9

A catalogue record for this book is available from
the British Library.

Designed and produced by Sandie Boccacci
on an Apple PowerMac 7500
Set in $9^1/2$/$12^1/2$pt Palatino
Printed and bound in Great Britain by
The Bath Press, Bath

Contents

Preface   7

Introduction   9

Session 1:
Healing Wounded Memories   13

Session 2:
Representational Confession   25

Session 3:
Family Group Story   37

Session 4:
Church Group Story   47

Session 5:
The Christian Day of Atonement   57

Session 6:
Community Group Story   67

Session 7:
Tribal and Nation Group Story   77

Books Related to Healing Wounded History   91

Preface

This book is the result of a journey of discovery that we have both been travelling along for some years. Michael and I met in the early 1980s when we were co-tutors on the Introduction to Pastoral Counselling Course that was pioneered through the Extension Studies Department at St John's College in Nottingham. Those days were ones of learning priceless lessons in caring for the whole person. It did not take us long to realise that in offering counselling to the individual we needed also to take into account the context of home, health and work situation which to some degree shaped the concerns and problems of the individual.

It was from this beginning that we began to see that the individual is precisely that individual because they are partially shaped by a number of group stories which they carry within them and from time to time articulate. Like all stories they contain elements that are good and which need celebrating and keeping but they also have wounds which need acknowledging and confessing. In this course, we have identified four basic groups as family, church, community and tribe or nation. Then came the challenge to explore whether there was healing for these group stories as well as the person who carries them. So began the adventure that has taken us around the British Isles and beyond with the opportunity to share our thoughts and offer ways of praying for wounded churches and families as well as working on the fronts of bringing reconciliation and renewal to communities and tribes which all too often repeat the unhealed patterns of their past. Consider the struggles in Northern Ireland, Kosovo and Rwanda as just three prominent examples of an unhealed past causing violence and pain in the present.

As we travelled around we were continually asked if any of this teaching was written down so that others could use it and share it with their churches. Consequently we have written this workbook for Christians who want to bring renewal to their churches and become a resource for the healing of their community's wounded group stories. Therefore the emphasis in this workbook is to offer some basic teaching followed by some practical work in which the insights offered can be gainfully applied to bringing healing at a group as well as an individual level.

RUSS PARKER
February 2001

Introduction

NOTES FOR COURSE MEMBERS

Welcome to the course! We are delighted you have decided to join a group and study this course, which we hope will be a healing experience for you personally, and for the groups that you identify with such as your family, church and local community.

You have in this course book brief summary notes of the teaching material, and also guide notes for the various activities that you will be doing. You won't need to read the Leader's Notes. We strongly recommend that you get a copy of Russ's book *Healing Wounded History*, which goes into the subject much more thoroughly and will act as a good resource for you as you learn about and engage in this particular aspect of the healing ministry. It would be good to read the relevant chapters in advance of each meeting.

You will see that there are seven sessions, six of which will be as a group, and the seventh (Session 5) will be done in your church building. Do try and come to every session, as they do connect together.

Finally, we do offer a 'health warning' about this course: during the sessions you are asked to explore not only your own memories, but the memory of your family, your church, community and nation. People are sometimes surprised at the strength of feelings that are engaged, even in memories that are not directly personal to them. Also, some people will be all too aware that in their own personal stories there are memories that are very painful. We do advise therefore that you take responsibility for the material you wish to share. By that we mean, where there are discussions and exercises that are about exploring memory, choose only material of your own story that you are willing to share. Don't feel under pressure to share that which you don't want to. Furthermore, be sensitive to others, who are also likely to have their own store of painful memories. This is a course where we need to listen well to one another and show Christ-like respect for each other. Having said all this, there will be obvious advantage in exploring our memories in the safety of the Holy Spirit, for there is no doubt that our Lord Jesus is the most tender surgeon whose desire at all times is for our good and for our healing.

We very much hope that through doing this course you will know the healing presence of God for you and the groups of which you are part.

NOTES FOR LEADERS

Use of course material
Each session has Course Notes for members of the course and Leader's Notes for the leader. You may wish to point out to the course members that they need not bother reading the leader's notes.

Teaching content
There is a block of teaching for each session. *Please encourage the members of your group to read these notes **before** the group meeting.* This will make a very big difference to your meeting. The group leader should not read out these notes verbatim from the script, but assuming that the group members have read the notes prior to the meeting, you should give a summary of the teaching, and then make use of the questions provided. Feel free to use these, or make up questions of your own.

Textbook
We strongly recommend that you purchase a copy of Russ Parker's major book on this subject, *Healing Wounded History* (DLT, 2001). This will provide much additional teaching material that is not in this course, and references to the relevant chapters for study are given at the end of each session. Course members will also benefit greatly from having their own copy of the book.

Some guidelines

1. The worth of this kind of exercise is maximum participation, so try to encourage as many as possible to share their own insights and observations.

2. Make sure that you have an OHP or flip-chart, or large sheets of paper, with the usual pens to write with. Ideally, have someone else to write down any comments offered within the plenary sessions so that you can concentrate upon inviting people to share.

3. One of the features of this programme is research, which is essential. You may like to appoint a research team whose task it is to look into the history of your church and the area it serves. This will be particularly helpful in advance of Sessions 4 and 6.

4. It is also important that the maximum number of folk within the church are involved in this course. This will be particularly important for the Christian Day of Atonement Service (Session 5).

5. Be alert for the sharing of conflicting stories and opinions. This is to be expected when exploring group issues, and the leader should resist favouring one story at the expense of another. Remember, it is the denied story, the one that is full of failure and that we cannot own publicly as ours, that usually stays longer in the memory and distorts behaviour. The object of the exercise is to listen to all the story and then together decide what to do in the light of this.

6. At the end of each session give a short summary of the work done and then remind people of next week's programme so that they can come prepared. Make sure that they are asked to read the relevant section of recommended reading from the textbook *Healing Wounded History*.

7. Each session is designed to last for an hour and a half, but you can tailor this to suit your group. You will find it helpful to look through the material and work out your own expected timing for each section of the session, so that you can be sure to complete the material by the end of the session.

Some groups doing this course have decided that they want to spend two weeks per session to give themselves a chance to cover the subjects thoroughly. The point is, make it *your* course and tailor it to suit the particular needs and concerns of your group.

8. You will see that the Christian Day of Atonement (Session 5) is designed to take place in the church, ideally with the whole congregation present. You will see too that we have placed this after the session on the church story, as it is a service that relates directly to the healing of the church. It is best done at this point when the teaching will still be fresh in people's minds, but practicalities may dictate that you have to do this service at some other time. Make sure it does not take place too long after the end of the course.

9. You will also need to give careful thought to the Prayer Walk in Session 6. There will be some advantage in people doing this before the meeting, as they can then give more time to it, and there won't be problems if it is pouring with rain on the day of your meeting!

10. Begin and end each session with prayer and worship as seems appropriate for you.

RUSS PARKER
MICHAEL MITTON

Session 1:
HEALING WOUNDED MEMORIES

Course Notes

> ### Outline for the session
> 1. The importance of memory
> 2. What's in a memory? (group work)
> 3. Memory and identity
> 4. An important memory and its consequences (group work)
> 5. An overview of group memories
> 6. Summary and close

1. THE IMPORTANCE OF MEMORY

(a) The biblical perspective
Old Testament

There are over 250 references to memory in scripture. As the bulk of the Old Testament refers to the story of a dispossessed or dominated people, anxious to maintain links with their homeland, it is no small wonder that their writings are full of encouragements to remember the land and how God had acted on their behalf both in and outside of that land of promise. **Remember** is the key word in the book of Deuteronomy which itself means 'second law.' This refers to the purpose of the book which is to look back at the shared story of the birth of the nation of Israel, but this time to see it from God's perspective and remember the lessons learnt.

Compare the following and note especially the use of the word **remember**:

- Deuteronomy 4:10–14: the giving of the covenant at Mount Horeb;
- Deuteronomy 5:15: the freedom from Egypt and the historical setting for the day of Sabbath;
- Deuteronomy 7:17–24: the motivation for entrance into and conquest of the Promised Land;
- Deuteronomy 8:2–9: reflecting upon how God led the tribes through the wilderness in order to prepare them for nationhood.

(For further optional study compare also Deuteronomy 9:27ff; 16:12f; 32:7.)

Such principles still hold true and we are not to forget this and let them slip when we experience our own difficult times. Consequently to **remember** is a call to identify with a shared story and to understand how the present life is to be or is still shaped by it. As far as the Old Testament is concerned our memory focus is to be upon God and the ways and purposes in which he acts for our benefit. To fail to **remember** means abandoning the Lord and his righteous purposes. It is to lose the point of the story which has shaped us, or even to distort that story.

New Testament
Similarly, the function of remembering in the New Testament is invariably to encourage faith and commitment to continue to follow God whatever the circumstances.

(a) Remember Jesus' witness and word: Matthew 27:63; Mark 14:72; Luke 24:8; 2 Timothy 2:8
(b) Remember in order to renew or heal: Matthew 5:23; 2 Corinthians 9:6; Hebrews 13:3
(c) Remember in order to pray accurately: Galatians 2:10; Philippians 1:3; 1 Timothy 1:3; Philemon 1:4

(b) Holy Communion

Another aspect of the importance of memory in the Bible is to be found at the heart of the Communion celebration. As he broke and distributed the bread to his disciples for the first and last time Jesus said, 'This is my body given for you, do this in remembrance of me' (Luke 22:19; cf. 1 Corinthians 11:23–6). Gerhard Kittel, in his *Theological Dictionary of the New Testament*, says that the act of remembering here is not the mere calling to mind or recollection of a past event or person, but takes the form of active representation as the action of Jesus is repeated. At one level the Holy Communion is a memorial feast, inviting us to identify ourselves with Jesus' crucifixion. At another level it is an opportunity to connect with the person of Jesus, who, from a human perspective, requests that we do this. As such it reflects his need to belong, to be a part of his gathered people. When we do so, he is truly alive and among us and we become complete in him.

It can be said, therefore, that remembering is an act of *re*-membering, of ownership and belonging between those who have the memory and the story and the people with whom we are connecting. For this moment both parties are alive to each other, if only in the act of remembering. However, it does underline that we are shaped by our memories and that the present and future to this extent are shaped by such memories.

(c) Distorted memory

As preparation for future exploration we need to signal that memories can be biased and inaccurate, and that sometimes they need to be substantiated by the facts revealed through research. Such distortions can be influenced by such things as **winner's**, **loser's** or **wounded memory**. If you watch a rugby match at Cardiff between England and Wales, for example, and for the sake of argument let us say that England wins, and then you ask a Welshman and an Englishman for their view of the game, it will be no surprise that you get two different understandings of the game. For the English it will be couched in the language of remembered triumph, but for the Welshman it will be riddled with sorrow at defeat by the old enemy. In other words, the memory of the game would link up with the old story of conflict and intrusion by the English on to Welsh soil. The loser's memory from ancient battlefields would shape the viewing of the game for the Welsh. Another example would be someone who finds it uncomfortable to open up their hearts to a lover because in childhood they were robbed of trust through some form of abuse.

We now need to explore what memories are made of.

2. WHAT'S IN A MEMORY? (GROUP WORK)

Consider this question:

> If you could unpack any memory, what ingredients will you find in each one?

Some examples:

> **feelings**
> **childhood**
> **beliefs**

The leader will write down the answers on an OHP or flip chart.

3. MEMORY AND IDENTITY

We could summarise all these comments by saying that all memories contain three major ingredients: **a story, a conclusion and a consequence**. As such, they underline that our memories are one of our chief ways of understanding who we are, and of determining our identity.

A story is my perceived account of something that affects me and touches me, however minimal. It will contain feelings which will exert some power and influence in my life and which will be triggered in present-day life by some event or other. It might be a word spoken in a certain way, or a smell which takes me back in time. The memory can be pleasant or it can be painful. But the important thing is that this is *my* story and as such it needs to be heard if I am going to live a whole life. Incidentally, it is always important to ask yourself how old you feel you are in this memory, as this might give you the clue as to how far back the story goes. When praying for healing it is often necessary to pray back into the beginning of the story as well as praying about the way that past story affects us in the present time.

A conclusion is the belief or decision we make about our self or another from that story, and usually this is the perception we live from as a result. If I was constantly told that I was a failure or 'could do better', and I believe this, then, no matter how much I may achieve, there will be a part of me that will never be pleased with myself and I will constantly push myself harder in order to attain that elusive feeling of being OK. If my family memories contain times of being affirmed and supported for who I am, then this is more likely to result in feeling confidence in God's cherishing care of me and this will stand me in good stead in days of uncertainty and testing. King David seems to have fed on these connections when he mentions innumerable times in his psalms how blessed he felt in the care of God for him.

A consequence is the lifestyle and expectations that we live out of and expect as a result of what we have concluded about ourselves from our memory. The Celtic peoples have a shared history of over six hundred years of being driven out of lands in which they settled. In a meeting in the Republic of Ireland a group of people were asked what was their greatest fear, and the unanimous answer was the fear of losing their land and their lives as a consequence. They still did not feel secure, even though they became an independent nation in the 1920s. The spectre of being dispossessed was still just beneath the surface. As a consequence the Irish have been described as one of the most possessive peoples in Europe.

4. AN IMPORTANT MEMORY AND ITS CONSEQUENCES (GROUP WORK)

After each person has shared, have a few moments to pray for each other for any healing you require for your story or for thanksgiving for the blessings that your story has contained. In turn, each person could offer their memory to God. This could take the form of using each hand as a focus for prayer. With whatever hand you write with, in this hand hold any part of the story you wish to renounce and let go of. You can symbolically give it away by opening this hand and placing whatever you wish to let go of, by faith, into the hand of the Lord. With your other hand you can symbolically hold on to that part of your story which has blessed and which you wish to retain. Then you can place this hand over your heart and the others in your group can ask the Lord to continue this blessing in your life.

5. AN OVERVIEW OF GROUP MEMORIES

So far we have been examining personal memories and stories. However, we also carry corporate or group memories as part of our make-up. This reflects the fact that from the very beginning God has created us for community. In turn, this is reinforced by the fact that the Godhead is a community of Father, Son and Holy Spirit. Consequently, it was not good for man to be alone and so a complementary and fulfilling partnership was to be found in his relationship with another (Genesis 2:18, 20–22). For good or ill, their relationship shaped their characters, choices and decisions. We are all, therefore, to some degree, a reflection of the community and places in which we have lived and shared. They shape us and we reciprocate by contributing to the shape of the community.

This tension and reciprocity between individual and group shaping is maintained throughout the scriptures. After the flood, the Bible describes the tribal leaders descended from Noah's three sons, Ham, Japheth and Shem, and speaks of them in terms of **clan**, **language**, **territory** and **nation** (Genesis 10:5, 20, 31). To understand the story and memories of each son you have to understand the fortunes of the clan, language, territory and nation. The rest of Scripture then focuses more particularly on one son, Shem, and the subsequent tribal clans, the territory of the Promised Land, the language of the Hebrews and the nation that is shaped by all these factors. The nation is called *son*, and even Matthew, to explain the significance of Jesus coming back to Israel from Egypt, refers to the text in Hosea 11:1 where he writes 'out of Egypt have I called my son' (Matthew 2:15). This theme of linking individual and group story is completed in the book of Revelation when God reveals that not only individuals will be redeemed through great battles, but also the people (group), language, tribe and nation of which we are a representative part (Revelation 7:9; 13:7; 14:6; 17:15). This does not mean that every nation or tribe will be saved, but that there will be something distinctive that God has invested in distinguishing each tribe and nation that will be celebrated before his throne in heaven.

Consequently, we are to take the group or corporate aspect of our lives seriously because it is important in the plans of God and is therefore to be incorporated into our strategies of healing and evangelism. We are therefore challenged to locate the group stories which we carry within us, of which we are a part, and to which we can make a contribution in care and renewal.

An example of an ancient community memory

A new incumbent to a group of churches in Suffolk noticed that no matter what community events he encouraged between the churches, all the churches took part except one which refused. Eventually the minister approached the warden of the abstaining church and asked him for an explanation. He was told it was because of the Vikings. As the minister looked puzzled the warden went on to explain what he meant. He pointed out that in the neighbouring parish they had a one-hundred-foot-high tower built in the tenth century, partly as a warning beacon to signal that the Vikings were approaching on one of their raids. This gave the people time to hide the church valuables and also themselves. There was one time when the Vikings did come and the neighbouring parish was alerted and managed to get to safety. However, they forgot to warn the people in the abstaining church, and many were killed and the church plundered. The warden concluded by saying that the people in his parish had never forgotten this and had never forgiven the people in the church with the high tower. The event was over nine hundred years old, but the memory and the conclusion and consequences made were still as fresh as ever. It seemed that the community were bound by common story to act in common even though many liked the new minister and, indeed, had friends in the neighbouring village. To a greater or lesser degree we all have this kind of loyalty to the group which on certain occasions changes our perspective from individual action to that of the group.

It seems that we all carry at least four group stories within us and they are as follows:

- family group story
- church group story
- community group story
- tribal or nation group story

Over the next four sessions we will be exploring these group stories and examining ways to identify them and bring a measure of healing and wholeness to them.

6. SUMMARY AND CLOSE

It will really help you if you can read through the notes for Session 2 before you next meet. In preparation for the meeting, give a bit of time to reflect upon your family story and see if you can locate some of its repeating patterns, both those which are a blessing and those which are wounded.

Further reading

Healing Wounded History: Chapter 1: 'Healing the Land: An Overview'; Chapter 2: 'Land as Gift and Sacrament'; Chapter 3: 'The Importance and Power of Memory'.

Leader's Notes

1. The importance of memory

Ask four people to read out the four passages from Deuteronomy. Use the following questions to help people understand the teaching:

(a) Why do you think remembering is so important?
(b) In the example of the England/Wales rugby match, why do you think the feelings can be so strong?
(c) Why do you think a loser's memory is stronger than a winner's memory?

2. What's in a memory?

Ask the group this question:

> If you could unpack any memory, what ingredients will you find in each one?

Some examples are given in the notes such as: **feelings, childhood, beliefs**. Remember, we are looking for general ingredients of a memory rather than a host of personal examples. Other such examples could be **story**, **connections**, etc. You might like to discuss the feelings that are identified and note the strength of them.

Encourage people to give one-word answers and write them down on an OHP or flip chart. Encourage people to expand on their comments. One way of doing this is to ask, **'Could you say more about that?'**

3. Memory and identity

Summarise the teaching, ask if people wish to make any comments, and see if they have any examples to share about:

- a powerful memory;
- a belief or decision made in the light of that memory;
- a lifestyle that is lived out in the light of that belief.

If people find it hard to think of personal examples, ask them about examples they have witnessed on TV etc (soap operas are full of examples!).

4. An important memory and its consequences

This group work is to help members of the group to connect what they are learning with their own life situations.

- Invite the group to split into groups of three (and a twosome if need be).
- Each person in turn will be invited to share a memory that they consider to be important. They must take responsibility for what they share, and at this stage of the course should be encouraged to avoid any memory that is too painful to share in the context of this short exercise. They have up to five minutes to tell the other two in their small group about this. The other two should listen carefully, but not interrupt the speaker.
- As group leader, give a signal when the five minutes is up.

One member of the listening pair will then ask these three questions (it may help people if you copy these three questions out beforehand and give them out to each group):

(a) What do you think is the most important part of the story you have shared?
(b) What conclusions have you made about yourself or anyone else from this story?
(c) What are the consequences you experience now from your story?

They have five minutes for this reflection.

- As group leader, now ask all the groups to be quiet. You may like to suggest that in their small groups they hold hands and offer prayer for the person who has just shared using the form suggested in the notes.

- When all three have shared, bring everyone back together as one group, and invite them to talk about how they found this way of working. You are not asking them to tell their stories and disclose information but to reflect on what it was like to be listened to and whether they made any discoveries about how their memories still shape them today.

5. An overview of group memories

Summarise the teaching and ask for comments and questions.

6. Summary and close

It is helpful at the end of each session to give a short summary of what has been learned during the session. For this session, you may like to offer something like the following:

(a) We have been looking at the importance and power of memories and remembering.

(b) We have seen that we carry both individual and group memories as a part of our human make-up.

(c) In order to bring healing, renewal and evangelism to the individual we have to give some time to understanding the group issues that affect them.

Encourage (strongly!) the group to read through the notes for Session 2. Also ask them, as preparation for the next session, to reflect upon their family story and to see if they can locate some of its repeating patterns, both those which are a blessing and those which are wounded.

REPRESENTATIONAL CONFESSION

Course Notes

> *Outline for the session*
> 1. The role of reconciliation
> 2. Representational confession
> 3. An act of representational confession (group work)

1. THE ROLE OF RECONCILIATION

Dr Rhiannon Lloyd, a former paediatrician from Rhyl, has been involved in a process of reconciliation with the Hutu and Tutsi communities in Rwanda that were so devastated by a period of horrendous inter-tribal warfare in the mid 1990s. Rhiannon's process for reconciliation involved asking the wounded to write down their worst experience. She then tells people to listen to one another's stories, not just to the facts but to the feelings within them. Then all the atrocities that have been written down and talked about are written on a large sheet of paper for all to see, and the group is asked 'What does God feel about this?' A big red cross is drawn over the sheet to symbolise that Jesus carried all our sins and hurts when he died on the cross. In the light of the cross of Christ, all are invited to make their response, telling God their story and sharing their pain and anger. People are also encouraged to nail their personal pieces of paper with their stories to a large wooden cross on the floor. The sound of the hammering is deafening, and yet the action of telling their story and expressing their pain in the presence of Christ who died for all has been proved time and again to be the pathway to reconciliation and healing. Following such a ritual, many have been able to forgive those who committed crimes of violence against them and their loved ones. The political leadership of the country now actively endorses these reconciliation seminars.

Rhiannon always begins these seminars by telling her own story, which involved a powerful moment of healing in her life. God disarmed her of her own resentment towards the English when some English Christians, on behalf of their forebears, confessed and apologised for the crimes of oppression they had committed against her people.

It is the love of God that energises the whole reconciliation process. While we took the initiative to be estranged from God through our own sin, it was he who took the initiative to be reconciled to us. St Paul writes:

> All this is from God, who reconciled us to himself through Christ, and has given us the ministry of reconciliation; that is, in Christ, God was reconciling the world to himself, not counting their trespasses against them, and entrusting the message of reconciliation to us.
>
> (2 Cor. 5:18–19 NRSV)

The dynamics of reconciliation

Reconciliation is not an attempt to gloss over the wrongs permitted by perpetrators. Nor is it achieved by negotiation and bargaining. Godly reconciliation does not settle for an uneasy peace where the parties in dispute find ways to coexist. Christian reconciliation is based on the reconciliation wrought by the cross whereby the vast gulf between God and humans has been healed. It is a costly reconciliation.

The following are some of the essential elements if true reconciliation is to be possible:

- **Remembering:** We must be given room to recall our story and to tell it.
- **Lament:** We need to find expression for the hurt that has been caused by the conflict.
- **Confession:** Few of us are totally innocent in a conflict situation. The process of reconciliation requires appropriate ownership of guilt through confession, but it is a confession that leads not to judgement but to freedom because of Christ.
- **Repentance – the penitential lifestyle:** Where we have identified that we have sinned against others, we commit ourselves to a lifestyle that is living out our confesssion, fulfilling Jesus' words to 'love your enemy'.
- **Forgiveness:** The petition 'forgive us our sins, as we forgive those who sin against us' is at the heart of the Lord's Prayer. Forgiveness does not mean condoning the crime, nor excusing the perpetrator, but it is the act of letting go of the grievance.

Where the hurt is deep, this process is not easy and is very costly. But our Lord Jesus has shown us the way and empowers us by his Spirit to be ministers of reconciliation.

2. REPRESENTATIONAL CONFESSION

The church has a right to represent its community by mandate from God. In 2 Chronicles 7:14 (in the context of Solomon's prayer when he is dedicating the Temple, and the Lord's reply) we have the familiar text:

> 'If my people, who are called by my name,
> will humble themselves and pray and seek my face
> and turn from their wicked ways,
> then will I hear from heaven and will forgive their sin
> and will heal their land.' (NIV)

Let's take a closer look at the principles contained in this verse.

(a) The right of access to the community story
(i) The people of God pray for the healing of the land

The reference to land in Scripture invariably refers not just to the soil and environment but also to the human community on that land. Consequently the people of God are exhorted not only to deal with their own needs for healing but also to extend this to their community. If you look at the stories of the fall of humankind (Gen. 3) and the sin of Cain's murder of his brother Abel (Gen. 4:8–14), you will note that the end product is the same: the inability of the offenders and their descendants to take root or belong to the ground upon which the wound was made. It is also interesting to note that Genesis 4:10 describes how God listens to the wounded story and locates the place on which this story occurs. ('Listen! Your brother's blood cries out to me from the ground.') It is no wonder therefore that almost the last healing mentioned in the Bible speaks of the healing of the earth with the creation of a new heaven and a new earth (Rev. 21:1). Coupled with this is the account in Romans 8:23–25, which reminds us that the redemption of humankind is inextricably linked up with the final healing of the land and earth itself. Consequently we are committed to the healing not only of wounded story but also of the very place upon which such wounds have occurred.

(ii) Daniel confesses the story of the generations (read Daniel 9:4–19)

This passage underlines for us our right of access to wounded group story. In this example Daniel is praying for his nation and the prayer is described as a confession (v. 4). What is fascinating is the history he covers in his prayer. Before continuing we should remind ourselves that he himself is innocent of the sins he describes but he nonetheless includes himself in the story of which he considers himself to be a part. Consider the following quote:

> We have to learn how to heal our history. Not forget it, but heal it, in the full knowledge and acceptance of what has gone before. We have to learn how to accept responsibility,

without [necessarily] admitting personal guilt, for what our ancestors have done to others ... [C]an we accept a measure of corporate responsibility for the darker side of what has gone before?

(John Lucal, 'The Berlin Wall, 1992 and Beyond', *The Way*, Vol. 31 [January 1991], p. 56)

Daniel refers to 'kings, princes and fathers'. In other words he is looking back before the captivity and realising that not only the dead but the living are responsible for the sins of the nation. There had not been a king on the throne for almost 70 years. He even goes back nearly two hundred years to the destruction of the Northern kingdom of Israel (v. 7). In other words Daniel has identified a right of access to pray for this nation's wounded story precisely because he belongs to it himself. They are *his* people. For us to pray for a particular group story we need to ask ourselves if we have a right of access. It is no use confessing the sins of the Japanese against the British and others if we are not Japanese or were not born in that country. In other words, we do not have a right of access.

(b) The ingredients of confession
(i) Ownership
You cannot confess what is not yours. As a preliminary step, therefore, we need to own the wounded group story we are focusing upon as ours. Beginning prayer in this way prevents us from slipping into accusation and thinking it is intercession. For example, Daniel could have equally prayed something like,

'Oh Lord, look upon the sins of this people; see what they have done. If only they had followed your ways, Oh God, they would not be in the mess they are now. Please forgive them and restore them to your healing.'

However, this kind of prayer actually distances the one who prays from the ones in need. It is a way of saying that I do not belong to the problem. However, true confession entails owning something as mine: it is only then that I can confidently bring it to God in a confessional manner. It also involves an identification with, as opposed a standing apart from, the problem.

(ii) Offering: something to let go (confess)

In Daniel's prayer he is asking God to enable the nation to let go of their rebellion and to be delivered from the consequences of this, which they are reaping in their present circumstances, namely the ruin of the city and the life of captivity.

True confession involves letting go of the repeated cycle we have identified and asking God for healing and deliverance from the consequences.

(iii) Offering: something to keep (celebrate)

Confession involves owning up to the good as well as the bad. Daniel is careful to remind himself that part of the nation's story is the giving of the law of Moses and the deliverance from Egypt. He wants to keep this in mind, because it offers a resource and exhortation for renewal. Consequently, whenever we pray for a particular group story we need to ask ourselves what is good about that story and celebrate before God. What is not affirmed will shrink!

(c) A process for representational confession

We may already be clear what it is that we wish to confess in prayer. But if not, here is a process that is helpful. It offers three basic steps to help us to be open to God for what he wishes to reveal and challenge us with. This can be done by simply inviting the Holy Spirit to come and rest upon us and reveal his will. Then we can share together what God has laid upon our hearts and write it down to help us remember as we pray together.

Invite the Holy Spirit:

 (i) to remind us that we are the people of God and part of the priesthood of all believers who are called to bring the needs of the people to God;
 (ii) when we have established which group it is that we are

identifying with (e.g. our family, our church, our nation, etc.), to show us which part of the group story to focus upon;

(iii) to help us take responsibility for the particular group story in question, even if we may feel personally quite detached from it (e.g. an incident in the life of our church that happened 100 years ago).

When we feel we have heard, we may find it helpful to write it down.

(d) The prayer of representational confession

Once we have identified what it is that we wish to confess, we come to the time of prayer. In prayer we need:

(i) to be aware that we are now owning publicly, as part of our story, what God has revealed to us;

(ii) therefore to pray from the perspective of *we* and *our* because it is our story: even if it happened in the past and the crime was perpetrated by others, we as representatives of this group own the story and use 'we' rather than 'they', which pushes the story away from us. To many of us this will be a new and difficult way of praying. Notice how many times Daniel uses the words, *us*, *ours*, and *we*, and never *I* and *they*.

Example

We may have discovered that our family has a history where fathers never communicated or affirmed their sons. We may discover that it has a long history in our family line. We may wish to pray personally, but we also need to pray a prayer of representational confession. Our prayers may be something like this:

A personal prayer:

Lord, I forgive my father for being as he was and not loving me. Set me free from this legacy of being the unloved and help me to be a loving father.

A representational confession on behalf of my family:

> Lord, we are a family where fathers do not love their sons.
> Please forgive us for being like this and heal our sins and
> set us free to love our sons and all our children. Amen.

Learn to begin praying in this representational fashion when
praying specifically for group stories. This is *not* to disparage
praying for particular individuals in relationship to me, the individual. We need to note, however, that this is not the biblical
model when praying for a group story.

In the coming sessions we will apply this method to praying
for the groups of which we are part.

3. AN ACT OF REPRESENTATIONAL CONFESSION (GROUP WORK)

This could be done as a full group, but is best done by dividing
into small groups of three. In this exercise you will be invited to
say a prayer of confession as a representative of a group of which
you are part. It is a 'practice run', so don't be over anxious about
getting it exactly right, but follow the guidelines and allow the
Spirit of God to lead you.

(a) In turn, each person should say what group they wish to
    identify with. It may be your family, your town, your
    nationality, your church (local or denominational), or any
    other group of people who have a clear identity and history.
(b) Once you have each decided which group you are choosing
    to identify with and pray for, one person in the group should
    pray the following prayer:

> Come, Holy Spirit, and lead us now in our prayer of
> reconciliation. Remind each one of us that we are the
> people of God, and we have a right to come to you and

pray for ourselves and for the groups of which we are part. Now speak to us, and guide our minds to any part of our group's story where we have been guilty of hurting others, that we may bring it now to Jesus, who through his death on the cross, forgives and heals us ...

Allow a few moments of silence for listening to God.

(c) Then check with each other whether we have identified an area for confession and prayer. If someone's mind is a complete blank, don't panic! They can simply ask to pass on this, or pray a general prayer for their group.

(d) Now, in turn, make your confession prayer. Remember to pray along the lines of 'Lord, we are a people who ... and in our history we did this ... please have mercy on us and forgive us.'

(e) When all have said their prayer, one person should read out:

If my people, who are called by my name,
will humble themselves and pray and seek my face
and turn from their wicked ways,
then will I hear from heaven and will forgive their sin
and heal their land.

Allow a few moments of quiet to let the truth and liberation of this sink in.

(f) Check out if any in the group wish to take any action on the prayer they have made, and check how each person is feeling. If any are feeling vulnerable after this confession, the others in the group may offer to pray for them.

Further reading
Healing Wounded History: Chapter 4: 'The Powers that Shape Group Stories'; Chapter 5: 'The Role of Reconciliation'; Chapter 6: 'Representational Confession'; Chapter 7: 'Jesus, the True Representational Confessor'.

Leader's Notes

1. The role of reconciliation

Ask the group to read the story of Rhiannon Lloyd's ministry of reconciliation in Rwanda. Open a discussion of this subject. You may like to use the following or similar questions:

- What is your immediate feeling as you read about this process of reconciliation?
- Why do you think it is necessary to tell the story and to write it down?
- Why do you think people were enabled to go beyond their hatred to a place of reconciliation?

Then ask someone to read the quote from St Paul (2 Cor. 5:18–19). Ask the person to read the passage out slowly and clearly, and tell the group that there will be about three minutes of silence after it is read out for quiet reflection. Invite the Holy Spirit to speak to the group through this passage. After the three minutes, ask:

- Has God spoken to anyone through this passage?

Allow the discussion to flow from this as you feel appropriate, yet allowing this profound truth to sink in, that we are all entrusted with a ministry of reconciliation.

Now ask the group to look in their notes to the five elements of reconciliation (**remembering – lament – confession – repentance – forgiveness**). Check out that everyone understands each element (fuller details are found in Chapter 5 of *Healing Wounded History*). Lead a short discussion on this, using the following or similar questions:

- Would anyone like to share an example of where they have found using one of these elements helpful in the process of reconciliation?

- Are there any elements that are particularly hard?
- Why can it sometimes be hard to forgive?

Say to the group that in the first part of this session we have been looking particularly at how we as individuals move towards reconciliation. We are now going to look at a process of reconciliation that we use when we are acting as representatives of a group.

2. Representational Confession

Ask people to turn to p. 27 in their notes, as you are now going to go through this process of reconciliation. Use the following guide and questions to help them understand the main points. The purpose of this session is to help people really get hold of this way of praying, for we shall be using it regularly in the next sessions.

(a) The right of access to the community story
(i) The people of God pray for the healing of the land

- Ask one member of the group to read out the passage from 2 Chronicles 7:14.
- Ask another to look up and read out Genesis 4:8–14.
- Ask another to read Revelation 21:1.
- Now ask the group to offer comments and in particular ask: 'What do these passages tell us about our relationship with the land?'

(ii) Daniel confesses the story of the generations

- Ask one of the group to read Daniel 9:4–14 (please use a version such as the NRSV or the NIV which includes the important word 'confess').
- Summarise the main points, and read out the quote from John Lucal.
- Ask the group for comments and in particular ask: 'Why did Daniel need to make this prayer of confession'?

(b) The ingredients of confession

- Make sure people have understood **ownership** and **offering**.
- Ask for comments, and then tell the group that we are now going to look at how, practically, we do this prayer of representational confession.

(c) A process for representational confession

Point out that these steps help us to listen to God and to be guided by him for the particular area of our group history that needs healing.

(d) The prayer of representational confession

Go through these notes carefully, reading out the example prayers of the father. Make sure that people have grasped the difference between the first prayer ('Lord, I forgive my father'), which is a prayer for personal healing, and the second prayer ('Lord, we are a family'), which is the prayer of representational confession, praying as a representative of my group.

3. An act of representational confession (group work)

The notes give clear guidelines for a group exercise that is best done in small groups of three. Go through the guidelines with everyone before you set the exercise, and check they understand the process and are happy with it. This exercise will give some practice in praying in this way, a way which will be used again in the coming sessions.

After the exercise is complete, bring people back together again as one group and check out people's response to this way of praying. Before they leave, encourage them to read carefully the notes for the next session in preparation for your next meeting which will focus on the group story of the family.

Session 3:
FAMILY GROUP STORY

Course Notes

> ### Outline for the session
> 1. The individual and group stories
> 2. Family group story
> 3. Looking at my family (group work)
> 4. Summary and close

1. THE INDIVIDUAL AND GROUP STORIES

In the last session we were looking at how we as the people of God have a commission to pray for the groups of which we are part. We belong to a variety of groups, and the diagram on the following page illustrates this. It shows how, as an individual, each of us also belongs to a variety of communities each with their group story. In this diagram you can picture yourself at the centre. You have your personal story with its beginnings, middle and end. However, you are also connected to your **family**, **church**, **community** and **tribal story** which together help shape your identity. Each of these groups will have their memories and stories, much of which you will know consciously and a lot of which you will only know unconsciously. They will also connect with particular localities, the places where your particular group had its roots.

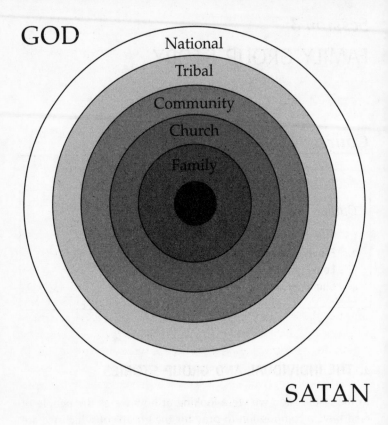

These stories may not always sit comfortably with each other. For example, if you are a mixture of English and Irish, then your story will often include stories and cultures that clash within you. If you compare stories of people born in the city of Liverpool with those from the city of Chester just 15 miles away, you will hear very different stories about environment, hope for development and self-regard. We also need to acknowledge that our group stories are touched by God as well as contested by the powers of darkness. In bringing healing and renewal to such accounts, we may need to offer to God for his blessing those parts of the story which are worth celebrating, and also confront the powers of darkness who seek to manipulate and hold on to the wounded and unhealed elements of our stories. All of these factors go into the making of us and form how we perceive ourselves. If we wish to bring the Gospel or healing to the individual more successfully, then we must take these issues into consideration and adjust how we present our witness accordingly.

Example of listening to a group story in the context of mission

In a recent mission audit in preparation for a city-wide witness to the city of Warwick, the church leaders noticed that there was one part of the city which was traditionally impervious to church ministry. In sharing the factors of that community it was discovered that historically the area was one of poor housing which had once been the home of the unwanted or the extremely poor. Although the area now consisted of new housing, it still felt like a place where people had been dumped. It seems that the memory of the communities down the years still lingered and affected the modern residents, although these had no family relationship to their predecessors. It was decided as a result of this that some form of apology needed to be offered by the church leaders to both the residents and the area itself for being so badly treated and neglected. This involved a prayer walk in the area, which included prayers of representational confession. Here Christian people were acknowledging that the people of their town had their own group stories, and for some who lived in a certain part of the town which had a history of pain, their lives were adversely affected because they were part of a group with a wounded history. In the following sessions therefore we shall be exploring some of the groups of which we are part. In this session we start with the one which is nearest for most of us: the family.

2. FAMILY GROUP STORY

Whether we are an only child, or come from a large group of siblings, or were adopted, we all have been shaped by our family group story. This will bring with it the usual mixed bag of good and bad memories. There will also be repeated patterns that we have inherited; we will need to be aware of these and pray about them in order to grow into more wholeness. In order to illustrate this point, look at the family group of Abraham: we will be looking at three generations. Before we begin, try to suspend the knowledge that you have of how God intervened in this family for his own sovereign purposes. This is not to undermine God's ways and designs but to enable us to focus upon the human story. We shall do this in the form of a shared Bible study.

Group 1: Abraham's family story

Read Genesis 16:1–5, 15–16; 21:1–11 and 22:2. Consider together the following questions:

(a) How would you describe the relationship of the parents with the children?
(b) How does this affect the relationship between the siblings?
(c) What is the end product of this story?

Group 2: Isaac's family story

Read Genesis 25:20–34 and 27:1–43. Consider together the following questions:

(a) How would you describe the relationship of the parents with the children?
(b) How does this affect the relationship between the siblings?
(c) What is the end product of this story?

Group 3: Jacob's family story

Read Genesis 35:22b–26 and 37:3–20. Consider together the following questions:

(a) How would you describe the relationship of the parents with the children?
(b) How does this affect the relationship between the siblings?
(c) What is the end product of this story?

What emerges from this study is a repeated pattern into which God brought his purposes and healing. The same will hold true for us and our family group story. If we do not spend some time recognising this for ourselves, then history will repeat itself in our family story until we acknowledge it and bring it to God for his healing. This is what we shall give some time to exploring now.

3. LOOKING AT MY FAMILY (GROUP WORK)

You will be asked to meet as a group of two. The group leader will tell you how long you have got. Make sure you both get a turn to share. You will have up to fifteen minutes each to share something of your family story. Please read together the following 'ground rules' which will help you in this time of sharing:

- Try and concentrate upon what you consider the most important details and essential moments.
- Please take responsibility for what you disclose. Be aware that sometimes this kind of exercise can touch upon personal material that might make you feel vulnerable because it still hurts and is painful. Do make sure that you share only what you feel is right for you to disclose. You may have some very unhappy experiences in your family, and we advise that you do not delve deep into anything that is likely to evoke too much personal pain, simply because there is not the opportunity in this exercise to give the time needed for such ministry. Ask for further help and follow up if you feel this would be appropriate.
- Keep confidential whatever is shared in your group. Through the time of sharing the listener will not interrupt with questions or advice unless it is for the purposes of clarification. The listener is there to help the person speak out what is on their heart, and they should not offer advice at this stage.
- You may find it helpful to have paper and pen handy to jot down some of the material you wish to bring to God for prayer.

The exercise
(a) The story
One person shares something of their family history, and the other person listens. If you are the speaker, you may choose anything from your family story, even if you want to go back several generations. See if you can notice particular patterns, and remember you want to locate things to celebrate as well as confess. If you are the listener, please listen without interrupting.

(b) Patterns
Once the sharing is completed the listener asks:

• What would you say are the main repeating patterns in your family story?

The speaker answers, and again the listener acknowledges but doesn't comment or ask questions.
Next the listener will ask:

• What is there to confess (let go of) and what is there to celebrate (keep) from your family story?

Again, the listener will acknowledge, but not comment.
If the speaker wants to discuss what they have shared with their listener at this point they may do so if it will help to clarify what part of their family story they wish to offer to God in prayer.

(c) Healing
The speaker now prays about what they have identified. Remember what we learned last time about representational confession. So the prayer should include 'we' and 'our'. For example:

> Lord, we are a family where the mothers and their daughters always seem to suffer from a lack of confidence. Please forgive us and heal us for not giving the women in our family a sense of belonging and affirmation. Lord, we celebrate that in our family we always had plenty of laughter and help us to keep a hold of this precious gift . . .

To conclude, the listener can then offer to pray for the speaker, to pray for their own personal healing and for the healing and blessing of that family. For example:

> Lord, I pray for this family of which N is a member. Bring your healing to this family ... Also I bless this family for its gifts of N and ask you to help these gifts grow and continue to bless this family in the name of our Lord Jesus Christ. Amen.

When this is complete, change roles so that the listener becomes the speaker and vice versa.

4. SUMMARY AND CLOSE

(a) We have been exploring the relationship between individual and group story.
(b) We have concluded that we are a mixture of both kinds of story that form a pattern of behaviour within us.
(c) We have examined the principle of representational confession as an element in the healing of wounded group story.
(d) Today we have concentrated on the family group story in order to understand ourselves and observed any repeated patterns to bring to God in prayer. In the next meeting we shall be studying how churches have group stories that may need healing.

Further reading
Healing Wounded History, Chapter 8: 'The Family Group Story'.

Leader's Notes

'Health Warning Notice'

In this session we explore memories and experiences from our family lives, including our childhood homes. Some people with painful memories of homes and families should be encouraged not to explore those memories that are particularly hurtful, because there simply is not time in this session to attend to hurts of this depth. Some may choose to miss this session if they feel they do not wish to risk touching on severe pain and trauma.

1. The individual and group stories

Ask people to turn to the diagram of concentric circles and then summarise the teaching from the notes, and point out the different community groups of **family**, **church**, **community**, **tribal**, **national (geographical, peoples, culture)**, **God and spiritual powers**. Ask the group:

- What are your reactions to this diagram?
- Are there other groups that you feel connected with?

2. Family group story

Divide your group into three. Allocate to each subgroup one of the Bible studies, so that one group studies Abraham, one Isaac and one Jacob. Ask them to turn to p. 40, to read the passage and to answer the questions. Tell them how long they have in their group.

Before continuing, mention to the groups that some times this particular study can touch upon parts of our personal stories that may still be vulnerable and hurting. Ask them to take responsibility for what they choose to share and not feel that they have to disclose anything about themselves that they are not ready to share.

When they have completed their studies, gather them back as one group again and ask each group to give a summary of the Bible story they have studied, and then to give their answers to the three questions. You may find it helpful to write their answers up on a flip chart to help compare them.

The three questions for each are:

(a) How would you describe the relationship of the parents with the children?
(b) How does this affect the relationship between the siblings?
(c) What is the end product of the story?

There is a common pattern to all three stories, and hopefully this will be apparent in the answers each group gives! Generally speaking a summary of each is as follows:

(a) How would you describe the relationship of the parents with the children? Answer: **Favouritism**
(b) How does this affect the relationship between the siblings? Answer: **Rivalry**
(c) What is the end product of the story? Answer: **Child leaves home**

Point out that this exercise shows how that for three generations in the family story of Abraham there has been the repeating pattern of parental favouritism, sibling rivalry, and a child leaving the family home. We each have a family story and it is likely to contain repeating patterns for good and ill. We have an opportunity to identify it. Where it is causing harm, we can confess it, and pray for healing so that it travels no further into future generations. Where it is a blessing, we can celebrate it and bless it to future generations.

3. Looking at my family

Please look through the exercise carefully before you ask people to do it. Although the instructions are clearly laid out on pp. 41–43, it will help people if you go through it with them. It may be best for you as a leader to stand out of this exercise, so you can keep an eye on how people are doing and help them if they need it. Also you can act as timekeeper, especially alerting them to when it is half time, so the listener can become the speaker and not miss their turn.

When the twosomes have finished you can gather people back together as one group and ask how people found the exercise. You may need to allow quite a bit of time for people to debrief this.

4. Summary and close

Read out this section from the Course Notes and close the session with prayer. Remind them to read the notes for Session 4 before you meet again.

Session 4:
CHURCH GROUP STORY

Course Notes

> ### Outline for the session
> 1. How churches evolve and grow
> 2. Researching the church's story (group work)
> 3. Owning the church's story (group work)
> 4. Summary and close

1. HOW CHURCHES EVOLVE AND GROW

Every church has its story of how it began, who founded it, and out of this a pattern of its life has emerged. This will contain its strengths and weaknesses and, importantly, will reveal its repeated patterns which still affect the church today. For example, if a church has been founded to cater for an influx of new labourers to the community (e.g. miners, railwaymen and other labourers for forms of heavy industry), while the main parish church continues to look after the older and sometimes better off among the community, then it often results in the new church rivalling the old. This is because the new church has in its foundational beginnings the feelings of being second class and/or being excluded from belonging to the community of the older church. Consequently the younger church sets out to prove that it is just as good as, if not better than, the original. This can result in a more extreme or aggressive form of life. The church becomes more catholic than its catholic original or it adopts a form of evangelical witness that somehow irritates its parent church. In other words the church's group memory is based on feeling left out and this influences its subsequent lifestyle and will go on doing so until it is acknowledged and brought to God for healing.

Example from Ireland

An example of this is that of a church in the west of Ireland which was Church of Ireland. Although the current rector was well liked in the community, it seemed that his church congregation was isolated from the rest of the community and not well liked. In researching the story of his church he discovered that a former incumbent had been fiercely anti-Catholic. With the Catholic Emancipation Act in the first half of the nineteenth century, the Catholic fathers of the community approached that incumbent, as he also held in trust the ownership of the land around the village. They wanted to purchase some land to build their own church. According to the popular story this incumbent took a coin from his pocket and threw it as far as he could into the bog which ran around the foot of the hill on which the town was built. He then told the Catholic fathers that they could have that piece of land. Without being deterred, the Catholic townsfolk set about draining the bog which took many years, and then built a church. Slowly but surely the population of the town gradually moved downhill and around the Catholic church so that the church on the hill became isolated from the community. Subsequently during a Communion service in the Church of Ireland, the minister apologised for the attitude of the church towards their Catholic neighbours and asked God to heal the church from this stain in its past. He noticed that this was the time when the church became more spiritually alive and that his attempts to develop better relationships between the churches in the town really began to grow.

Listening to the story

For the healing and renewal of the church we need to understand how wounded stories, no matter how old they be, still exert a power to shape the present. We need to understand this story and see how this group memory of the church's life is being repeated today. As the poet Steve Turner writes in his book *Up to Date*:

History repeats itself,
It has to,
Because nobody listens.

This is brought home very vividly in the prophetic words of Jesus to the seven churches in Asia Minor mentioned in Revelation chapters 2 and 3. Each church is addressed in a particular way with a threefold structure. Consider the following example in the address to the church at Ephesus:

- a summary of the church's story (2:2–3);
- a challenge and a consequence by the Lord of the church (2:4–6);
- an exhortation and a promise (2:7).

So the first step towards healing for the church's story is to listen accurately to that story and discern its repeated patterns down through the years and in its present-day manifestations.

If we look again at the passage referred to earlier in 2 Chronicles 7:14, we will see that before the healing of the land there comes the healing of the people of God. God first listens to the confession of sins of the people, then heals them, and then moves on to heal the land. What this tells us is that the healing of the community is to a major degree dependent upon the healing of the group story of the people of God. Therefore, a priority in all our concerns for mission to the community or revival in the land, is the healing and delivering of the wounded group story of the people of God which in the New Testament is none other than the church of Christ. What this passage also tells us is that it is only the healed people of God who have this God-given mandate to bring healing to the land. Consequently we must focus our attentions on healing for the church. The church must be reconciled to its own group story before it can an ambassador of reconciliation and healing to its community. This is why, when considering mission to our community, we need to ask ourselves if the church, at this moment in time, is part of the problem or part of the solution for its community.

An example from the Midlands

One incumbent, for example, reported that his community seemed apathetic and distrustful of the church's attempts to be a resource for care and mission. In researching the story of that church he discovered that the community was founded on the forceful removal of coalminers from their homeland and tied houses in the North to work in the new pits being opened in the Midlands. In order to keep this rather disgruntled community in good working harmony the mine owners gave patronage for a church to be built, which all the workers and their families were expected to attend. Far from the church being regarded as a pastoral resource, many regarded it as the policeman of the community. This feeling had persisted even after 150 years in the ongoing memory of the community. As a result the minister, on behalf of the church authorities, apologised to the congregation for forcibly removing them from their homeland and making them attend the church. He asked them for their forgiveness. Even though many of the present-day congregation were not related to this former community, they nonetheless recognised such feelings among themselves and there was a noticeable change in the way the church began to feel about itself, and the community became more responsive to its ministry.

So we can see that one of the prime requisites for mission is healing for the church's wounded group story. At the heart of this process is the need to research the church's story, observe the repeated patterns, own the story in a confessional manner and consider an appropriate form of public apology. We now look at this in more detail.

2. RESEARCHING THE CHURCH'S STORY (GROUP WORK)

Questions for group discussion and research:
(a) What is the history of our church?
Helpful pointers:

- Who founded the church?
- What was their spirituality and why? Was it to suppress a conflicting spirituality (e.g. high church versus low church)?
- Was there a special reason for founding the church?
- Do you know anything about the story of the site on which the church was built?
- Were there other churches already in the community? If so, what was or is the relationship between those churches? Was your church to complement or to compete with the other churches?

(b) What are the recurring patterns of our church's story?
Helpful pointers:

- Splits in the fellowship.
- Breakdown in relationships between congregation and minister.
- Repeated opposition to mission, renewal etc.
- Cycles of sickness among key members.
- Lack of self-worth or expectation of blessing.
- Reproduction of community problems in the life of the church.

(c) Where have these patterns occurred?
Helpful pointers:

- Is there some geographical part of the community that the church serves where these patterns are located?
- What is the story applicable to that site?
- Does it in any way correspond with the repeated pattern?
- How does this part of the community respond to the church's ministry in comparison with other areas?

(d) If you could imagine the angel of your church describing how it feels to be the angel of your church, what would the angel say?

Helpful pointers:

- This is based on the fact that Jesus addresses the angel of the church in Revelation and challenges it with the story of the church and its need for healing.
- It is an exercise in being open to the Holy Spirit to put us in touch with the feelings and events ongoing in the life of the church.
- Do not be anxious that this is a subjective exercise, as we can check out the facts of the feelings with what we share with others of the known story of the church.

3. OWNING THE CHURCH'S STORY (GROUP WORK)

Guidance for praying in groups
(a) Identifying a repeated pattern of the church's story

- Before praying, focus on a particular part of the church's story which has struck you as being significant.
- Remember, that as a member of this church, you have a right of access to this story no matter how old it is.

(b) The prayer of representational confession

- Now offer this part of the church's story to God in confession.
- Remember to use the words *we* and *our*. This avoids falling into accusation and blaming others for the problems of today. It also encourages identification rather than distancing yourself from the issue that needs healing.
- The following is a model of the kind of prayer you may wish to use:

Lord, please forgive us because we are a church where we ...
(state the repeated pattern).
Please heal us and deliver us from this and help us to walk in newness of life. Amen.

Please feel free to expand upon this prayer as you think suitable.

- There may also be things about the life of the church which are a blessing and these too need to be offered in prayer, but this time in thanksgiving. What is not celebrated shrinks for lack of affirmation. Therefore you may want to pray a prayer after the following model:

  Lord, we thank you because we are a church which is blessed by ... *(state the thing which is a blessing in your church).*
  Please increase this blessing among us so that our church may continue to grow. Amen.

4. SUMMARY AND CLOSE

(a) We have explored and shared how our church began, and clarified some of its repeated patterns which are both blessings and wounds in today's church.
(b) Having identified these repeated patterns we have brought them before the Lord using the form of prayer known as representational confession.

Further reading
Healing Wounded History, Chapter 9: 'The Church Group Story'.

Leader's Notes

Before the meeting make sure you have prepared the four acetates/flip-chart sheets with the four areas of research from section 2 clearly written, one at the top of each sheet, as follows:

1. The history of our church
2. The current recurring patterns
3. Where the patterns have occurred
4. The angel of the church

For a more thorough job, you may wish to split this session into two, devoting the first meeting to the research (which could continue through the week), and the second to feedback, identifying patterns and the representational prayer.

1. How churches evolve and grow

Summarise the teaching. You may like to choose one of the churches addressed in Revelation chapters 2 and 3, and ask someone to read it out. Point out the pattern of how the church is addressed (points a, b, and c in the course notes).

Ask someone else to read 2 Chronicles 7:14, a text with which the group should now be familiar. Point out that:

• before the land can be healed, the people have to be healed;
• the healing of the community is dependent on the healing of the group story of the people of God;
• the healing of the church therefore opens the way for mission into the community.

Ask the group if they are beginning to understand this principle. You may like to refer them to the two examples from Ireland and the Midlands and see if they have any comments about these stories.

After this discussion, your group will now be involved in two long pieces of work: the first is to do some thinking about the history of your church, and the second is to engage in an act of representational confession as together you own that story. At the beginning of this course you may have asked someone to do some research on your church, and you may find it useful to have on an acetate or flip chart a summary of their findings.

If you have people from different churches in your group, try and form groups that consist of people from the same church. If there are individuals from churches, then you can form one 'mixed church' group, in which each person will need to discuss their own church story, with the others offering reflections. Such groups can be very valuable for comparing stories, and noting parallels.

2. Researching the church's story

Ask your group to join hands and say a prayer asking for the guidance of the Holy Spirit on all that is to be shared and revealed. The joined hands are to demonstrate that everyone is an integral part of this work and that it is the one church at work here.

After the prayer, ask people to form groups of about three or four, and ask them to nominate one of them to write down the findings of the group.

Now guide them through the four sections, allowing up to 15 minutes for each section. Read out each question and run through the helpful pointers expanding upon them as you see fit, though don't take too long on this or else you will deprive them of discussion time. When you come to the fourth question about the 'angel of your church', you may wish to have a few moments of silence as they wait on the Holy Spirit to help them to focus on the message of the angel of their church.

At the end of the group discussion (which will have taken about an hour in total), give about 15 minutes to receive comeback from the group. Use the four acetates or flip-chart sheets that you prepared before the meeting with the four areas of research written at the top of each sheet. As groups give feedback to you, write down their findings.

Having done the research, you are now going to offer it to God in prayer.

3. Owning the church's story
If your group is much larger than 12, then it will probably be easiest to break into two or more groups.

Follow the instructions in the course notes:

(a) Identifying a repeated pattern of the church's story
Try not to spend too long on this. Hopefully between you, you will be able to identify a clear pattern that you want to bring to God. Ensure you draw out things about the church's story which are a blessing – this is essential for retaining a balanced sense of events.

(b) The prayer of representational confession
Follow the guidelines in the notes. As the leader you may want to pray first to demonstrate the kind of praying you are inviting. So, for example, if one of the repeated patterns is that the ministers have never really got on with their congregations, then the kind of representational confession would be:

> Lord, please forgive us, because we are a church where ministers have never really got on with their congregations. Come now and heal and deliver us from this so that we can grow and walk in newness of life. Amen.

4. Summary and close
After the prayer time has finished, invite comeback from the group about how they have found the exercise. Be aware that the next session in the course notes is 'The Christian Day of Atonement.' You may have chosen to do this as part of your Sunday worship. Whatever you have decided, give the group clear instructions about what will happen in the next meeting.

Session 5 :
THE CHRISTIAN DAY OF ATONEMENT

Course Notes

A LITURGY FOR THE CHURCH'S STORY

In the Old Testament there is a healing service whose sole aim is to release the place of ministry to be what God intended it to be. It is called the **Day of Atonement**. The Hebrew word for atonement is *kippur* and according to William Gesenius, a Hebrew scholar, this word means 'to be delivered from the effects of'. What is intriguing is the historical reason for the institution of this healing rite for the building (originally the Tabernacle) and for the ministers and ministry they are called to offer: it is the breakdown of leadership and their work and the consequent effects on the spiritual health of the community of faith and the effectiveness of the house of the Lord.

Leviticus 16 begins with this statement, 'The Lord spoke to Moses after the death of the two sons of Aaron who died when they approached the Lord.' The two sons in question were Nadab and Abihu, who had fallen dead before God because there was something seriously wrong in their lives when they offered their ministry in the tabernacle. They had sought to bask in the same power and glory of God which had come upon Moses and Aaron when they had gone before the Lord in the tabernacle. They went through exactly the same motions of ministry but their motivations were all wrong, their hearts were full of pride and so the fire of God consumed them (Lev. 9:23—10:3; Num. 3:2–4). What is so devastating was that the effects of their ministry made invalid that of their father, the High Priest, and also the building itself. All needed to be cleansed.

What follows is a detailed rite for the cleansing of the place of ministry and those who offer it. First there was to be cleansing for the High Priest and his family (Lev. 16:6, 11), even though Aaron was not present and had taken no part in Nadab and Abihu's rebellion. However, he is affected because he is connected to the same family and ministry group story. This is what the Old Testament understands by *corporate* or *group* story. Next, atonement was to be made for the Most Holy Place which was not even entered by Nadab and Abihu because only the High Priest was allowed to enter there. Yet ministry offered in the place of ministry affects the whole building and so it too needs cleansing. There then follows a cleansing for the whole ministry of the building and this is supremely focused on the altar itself (Lev. 16:19, 24, 29, 30). God also decreed that this become an annual event for the good of the people and their worship. It is clear from this that the Day of Atonement was not only a response to a particular need to release and renew minister and congregation alike, but also a resource for ongoing healing and forgiveness within the whole community on future occasions.

What we must ask ourselves is whether this procedure is only applicable to the Old Testament tabernacle and Temple or whether it holds true for every place of ministry for the people of God. I suggest that here we have a principle and liturgy of healing for every place dedicated to God and his ministry. Consequently it becomes a powerful resource for the healing of wounded church stories. However, because of the once-for-all sacrifice of Jesus on the cross, it is to be carried out through the name and power of Jesus and not the old covenant sacrifice of animals. Therefore, as part of the healing and renewal of the church, we may need to hold a Christian Day of Atonement. The following is a rite that many are finding helpful.

THE CHRISTIAN DAY OF ATONEMENT SERVICE

Opening Sentences

LEADER Behold how good and pleasant it is when we live together in unity.

ALL **It is like the oil of the Holy Spirit poured on our heads.**

LEADER Here is the place where God will command his blessings for us, even life for evermore.

ALL **Amen.**

Collect of Invocation

ALL **O God our Father, we praise you**
that you have made your Son, Jesus Christ,
Lord of our church.
Come now by your Holy Spirit
and set our hearts on fire with love for you
and one another.
Renew our church
to be a powerful witness in this community
as you bring the healing of your forgiveness
amongst us,
through Jesus Christ our Lord. Amen.

Worship time

Suggested Readings
Psalms 15; 24; 32; 85
OT Leviticus 16
Ezekiel 45:17–20
Isaiah 55; 64
NT Matthew 18:21–35
Luke 18:8–32
2 Corinthians 2:5–11

Homily

Affirmation of faith

Nicene Creed *(said or any sung version)*

Penitence and Confession

LEADER   Our Lord Jesus Christ calls us to be a people
who know how to forgive one another.
Let us then come humbly and boldly into his light
so that we may first receive forgiveness for our sins
and then offer this freedom to those who have hurt us
in some way.

ALL   **Our loving, heavenly Father,
you have shown yourself to be a forgiving God
who has gone out of his way to the cross
where you shouted loud and clear
through the wounded heart of your Son, Jesus Christ,
that we can be freed and cleansed
from all our wrongdoings and misdeeds.
We are sorry and ashamed of our sins
and for the sake of your dear, firstborn Son,
ask that you forgive us for all that lies in the past,
and that you lead us out of our sickness
into the health of your healing presence. Amen.**

LEADER   Almighty God forgive you/us and cleanse you/us
from all unrighteousness,
in the name of our Lord Jesus Christ
and through the power of the Holy Spirit
coming upon you/us now.
So rejoice, for your/our sins are forgiven and
you/we are cleansed and released!

ALL   **Thanks be to God! Alleluia!**

Forgiving others

LEADER   Having received God's forgiveness,
we are now open to forgive those
who have hurt or troubled us.
Let us be still and let God show us
those whom we need to forgive and release.

*Suggested method: Write down on a piece of paper the names of those in
your church you wish to forgive. Then fold the paper and place it in a
basket on the altar. There can be some gentle singing while time is given
for people to come forward.*

LEADER   *(holding up the basket to God)*
Dear Lord, look on the lives
of all those we have named here.
Help us to let go of them
and all the hurts that we have carried from them
and between us.
We free them from our past spirit of unforgiveness.
Send out your Holy Spirit upon them
and heal and renew them in the love of Christ
and the power of your Holy Spirit. Amen.

Sharing the Peace

A time of greeting each other and saying:
'The peace of Christ be with you.'

Prayers of cleansing for the church

LEADER   Now that the Lord has renewed our unity in the Holy
Spirit, it is time to ask him to deliver our church from
anything that has been said and done down the years
which still grieves the Holy Spirit. Let us then all
gather together around the various places where the
life and ministry of our church is focused.

The congregation will now gather and pray in such places as:

> *the pulpit and/or minister's seat*
> *the communion table and/or rail*
> *the baptismal font*
> *the choir stalls or musicians' seats*
> *the wardens' seats*
> *the vestry*
> *the entrance to the church*

Closing prayers and worship

Further reading
Healing Wounded History, Chapter 10: 'The Christian Day of Atonement'.

Leader's Notes

1. Preparation

Before you start the service, have a short time of preparation to establish that people are clear about what it is they are engaging in during this service. Refer them to the teaching in their course notes. Ask them if they have any questions about the notes. Do not draw the discussion out as you want to give the main part of the session to the service. You may like to conclude with a short service of Holy Communion which will have the effect of sealing the work that has been done and establishing the sense of community that will inevitably be felt during this liturgy.

2. The Christian Day of Atonement Service
General points

(a) The suggested liturgy is only a guideline and may be altered according to your own preferences.

(b) The service is best used in your church building and ideally should include as much of your regular Sunday congregation as possible. If there are people present who have not been part of the group study, then you will need to give them a very brief summary of what you have learned in the previous sessions, so they are clear about the purpose and nature of the service.

(c) The timing of the service will depend greatly on how you lead it, and how involved people become. As leader you will know how long your folks are comfortable with, so you decide the length. It is advisable to allow a few minutes at the end for comments and reflection.

(d) The people should be well prepared before they come to this service. They should at least be asked to pray beforehand about any person or issue they need to acknowledge and forgive, in anticipation of the personal confession and forgiving of others that takes place at the beginning of the service.

(e) Include any songs or hymns for worship as you require, preferably ones that are well known so that people are not distracted by having to learn new songs and hymns.

(f) The homily should be fairly short and focus on the subject of healing for the church's story and the ministry of forgiveness.

(g) When people write out their private list of people to be forgiven, do assure them that the papers will not be read but destroyed after the service.

(h) Remind the people that, when they come to pray for anything connected with the various places that need prayer, to use the representational form of prayer using the words 'we' and 'our'. This may feel strange to some, but encourage them to try it out. Remind them that we are owning our story and stand as representatives of our church community down the ages.

Times of prayer – some helpful hints

(a) The leader should keep an eye on how the prayers are forthcoming (or not), and occasionally encourage people to share their prayers if there is too long a lull in the proceedings. She or he should help everyone to be relaxed and open to spontaneity in their praying and sharing.

(b) When you begin to pray at various places within the church, invite everyone to gather around as close as possible so that when they pray out loud they will be heard.

(c) When praying over the role of the minister (or ministry team) it may be useful to encourage the people to lay hands upon them and offer prayers of apology and blessing.

(d) When praying at various ministry places, you may like to encourage people to lay hands on these places as a sign of God's blessing. If the group is large, then let people lay hands on people who are able to lay hands on the various places. You may want to anoint some places and items of furniture (e.g. the organ console, choir stalls or pulpit) and rededicate them for future use. For example it may have been shared that some of the preaching in the church has been hurtful or erroneous. Invite the current minister to stand in the pulpit and pray in a representational-confession way for forgiveness and healing for being a church which has not brought God's caring word to the church. If there has been division in the church, invite the current leadership team to ask for forgiveness. The congregation can respond by blessing the leadership team and asking God to heal both leaders and congregation from the wounds of division.

(e) Depending on how familiar people are with charismatic spirituality, you may want to encourage them to be open to prophetic words or words of scripture, and to share them as you pause for prayer at the various stations within the church.

(f) The leader will need to gauge when they think there has been sufficient prayer at each station, and then encourage the group to move on to the next place.

Example of the kind of prayer that might be prayed in the pulpit

Lord, we are aware that we are a church where we have often criticised our preachers, leaving them feeling vulnerable and lonely. Because we have been suspicious of them, we have closed our ears to your word. Please have mercy on us, forgive us and heal us, and help us to listen with new ears that are not distorted or deafened by our past history, but are open to your loving and life-giving Spirit. Amen.

3. Conclusion

At the end of the service you may like to spend a few minutes asking how people felt about the service and to offer any reflections and comments.

Encourage people to read the notes in Session 6 in preparation for your next meeting. Please note there are a lot of Bible references in Session 6. Reassure your people that they are not expected to wade through them all! They can choose those that interest them.

For the future, you may like to consider whether you would like to hold an annual Christian Day of Atonement Service.

Session 6:
COMMUNITY GROUP STORY

Course Notes

> *Outline for the session*
>
> 1. The Bible and the city
> 2. Jesus in the city (group exercise)
> 3. Mapping out your community (group work)
> 4. Ministry to the community
> 5. Summary and close

1. THE BIBLE AND THE CITY

From the very beginning of our creation God has made us for community. Beginning with his purposes for Adam, the Bible reveals a pattern of development for human growth which includes belonging to community. From Adam there is the growth of Patriarchal families, which leads to the formation of tribes, which results in the nation of Israel. The nation and society is then understood in terms of city life. There are at least 1,400 references to cities in the Bible. Naturally we should not understand cities of the Bible as like the modern metropolitan cities with their urban sprawl and decay; they were on a much smaller scale, but were nonetheless communities with their own particular group story and memories. In particular, city life in the

Bible is focused on the relative spiritualities of Jerusalem and Babylon. Jerusalem is the city of God and Babylon is the city abandoned to self-centredness. All this is consummated in the final healing mentioned in Revelation, which is the creation of the new Jerusalem, the city in which God is the light and life of its people (21:1f).

What then is God's relationship with the city?
(a) God wants to live in the city
Of the 150 psalms, 49 are city psalms. Psalm 42:1–2 paints the picture of God dwelling in the middle of the city. Psalm 46:1–3 describes the presence of God defending the city from its enemies. Psalm 122 contains an exhortation for the faithful to go about the walls of the city and proclaim the peace of God to the very buildings as well as the community. Here we have the first example of the prayer walk! In Ezekiel we have a picture of God wooing the city like a lover longing for his bride (16:1–14).

(b) God calls the city to be a place of social and spiritual harmony
'Listen! the Lord is calling the city' (Mic. 6:9). The Bible is full of references to the fact that the city or community is the central feature or model for a restored land. The prophets constantly challenge and exhort the city to live up to its God-given calling to be a place of refuge, a home for justice and a witness to the love and care of God (cf. Isa. 26:1–6; 60:12; 65:17–25; Ezek. 48:35; Mic. 5:2; Zech. 2:4–5).

(c) The city is the focus for the power of God
Jesus' ministry has a significant urban dimension. It was in the cities of Korazin, Bethsaida and Capernaum that most of his miracles were performed (Matt. 11:20). The Apostle Paul confined his mission almost exclusively to cities as they were the heartland of the nations. The church is described as a city on a hill, whose light is to penetrate and permeate the community. Perhaps we need to say in response to this that there is only one community and that the church is the beating heart of it.

God also treats the city as a single group personality. For example, when prophesying against the nations, Isaiah often addresses the ruling cities of those nations:

- Babylon for the nation of Babylonia (Isa. 14–15);
- Ar, Kir and Dibon for the nation of Moab (Isa. 15:1–4);
- Damascus for the nation of Assyria (Isa. 17);
- Jerusalem for the nation of Judah (Isa. 22).

Also, what affects the individual or family affects the whole community:

- The ten righteous who could have saved the cities of Sodom and Gomorrah (Gen. 18:16–33);
- The idolatry of a group brings judgement on the whole city (Deut. 13:12–18).

A modern-day example of this is the terrible murder in Liverpool of James Bulger by two young boys. The murder of the little boy affected the whole community in the Walton area of Liverpool. People totally unconnected with the event felt responsible because such an awful thing had happened among them.

From these observations we can conclude that we are shaped by the spiritual and moral personality of our community, and that God will hold us as individuals, as well as a city group, responsible for the life and pattern of our shared story. Far from being distant from our communities, therefore, the church is part of the story of the city and has a responsibility to be a resource for its healing and wholeness. If we are going to be effective in our witness as a church we must become familiar with our city group story and own it as our story too.

2. JESUS IN THE CITY (GROUP EXERCISE)

Most of Jesus' ministry was carried out in the towns and cities of his day. He stood and preached in the market-places, synagogues and the Temple itself. He was also tried and condemned in the city and finally crucified outside the city walls. We shall now examine some of the ways Jesus conducted his mission in the city, how he related to its life, and the use he made of its buildings.

Preparation

- Select one person in your group to read out the Bible passage slowly.
- Select another person to read out the questions for each section.
- Select another person to write down the findings.

(a) Jesus, witness to community story: Matthew 23:37–39; Luke 19:41–44

Jesus summarises the city's history and its current consequences and challenges it to wake up to what is happening and be open to the blessings of God. Questions:

- What is the story of Jerusalem according to Jesus?
- How far back does he go with this story?
- What solutions, if any, does Jesus offer for the city's healing?

(b) Jesus, listener to community story: Matthew 24:1, 2; Mark 13:1, 2

Jesus has a perspective different from that of his disciples to the story wrapped up with the temple building. Questions:

- Why do Jesus and his disciples have a different insight to the significance of the same building?
- What are the important buildings in your town and what is their significance?

(c) Jesus, celebrator of community story: Mark 12:1–4

Jesus, in the doomed city of Jerusalem, singles out the generosity of heart of the poor widow. Questions:

- Why does Jesus celebrate the widow?
- What is the value of celebrating such actions?

- Is there anyone or anything you want to celebrate about your community?

(d) Jesus, healer of wounded places: John 9:7; Luke 13:1–5

Jesus sends the man born blind to a wounded place to receive his healing. Questions:

- What is the story of Siloam?
- What effect, if any, do you think the healing of the blind man had on people's impression of Siloam?
- Is there a wounded place in your community?
- If so, what is its story and how may it be healed?

3. MAPPING OUT YOUR COMMUNITY (GROUP WORK)

This is an opportunity to understand and pray for our community. It is essential that we learn to do this if we are going to be a resource for mission and healing to our society. Before actually going out into your community in any form of ministry, it is important that we properly prepare.

The following are some helpful pointers to help us be ready. Before beginning, decide what is the manageable area of community on which you will focus your ministry. For example, if you live in a city, you may prefer to select an area of the city, rather than the whole city. If you live in the country, decide whether to select your village, or perhaps two or three villages that consider themselves part of the same community.

(a) Research the history

 (i) How and by whom was your community established?
 (ii) Do you know anything of their character and belief?
(iii) What are the outstanding historical events of your community?
(iv) Are there any events which are a blessing or a curse to your town?
 (v) Do any of their effects still remain?

(vi) What are the repeated patterns which still shape your community?

(b) Review the social life
 (i) What is the employment story of your community?
(ii) How would you describe the housing situation in your community?
(iii) Are there any areas of decay and neglect?
(iv) What parts of your community are warm and inviting?
 (v) What are the main political and social challenges?

(c) Reflect on the spiritual health of the churches
 (i) What is the relationship between the churches?
(ii) Is there any need of healing between them?
(iii) Which is the oldest church in your community and what is its story?
(iv) With what major civil functions and community sharing are you involved?

(d) Realise the nature of spiritual warfare
 (i) What is the general response to Christian witness?
(ii) Can you identify parts of the town where it is most difficult to witness?
(iii) What particular issues or feelings do you discern in these places?
(iv) If you had to summarise the emotions of your town story, what single word would you use to describe them?

4. MINISTRY TO THE COMMUNITY

Now we have an opportunity to put some of these insights into practice as we learn to minister to the needs of our community story. This will take the form of a prayer walk. We are encouraged in Psalm 122 to go about the city and proclaim peace within its walls. In faith and in the company of our risen Lord we will go into our community in small groups and try to put into practice some of the principles we have been learning about how Jesus ministered to his community. Afterwards, we will have an opportunity to share our findings together, and then to decide how to build upon what we have learnt.

5. SUMMARY AND CLOSE

We have looked at the importance of the city and of how God still has a desire to bring healing and renewal to communities.

We have learnt some principles of ministry to the city from the example of Jesus.

We then looked at our community and learnt something of its story.

Finally, we have gone into the city and tried to put into practice some of the lessons Jesus has taught us.

In our final session we will look at how tribal or national group story affects our lives and witness.

Further reading
Healing Wounded History, Chapter 11: 'The Community Group Story'.

Leader's Notes

This is a longer session than the others if you include the prayer walk (see Section 4). Decide well in advance if you want to include it in this session or whether you might break this into two sessions.

1. The Bible and the city

Encourage the group to read the material from this chapter before the meeting begins.

Invite different people from the group to read out some of the shorter passages or part of the longer references. Only choose some of the scripture references available and leave people to study the remaining texts privately if they wish.

With reference to the James Bulger story, ask for any other examples of an event which has caused the community to respond in a similar way. What can be learnt from these observations?

2. Jesus in the city

- Invite the people to divide up into small groups of about four or five.
- Refer people to the course notes 'Jesus in the city group exercise' on pp. 69f.
- One person in the group will read out the Bible passage slowly.
- Another person will read out the questions for each section.
- Another person will write down the findings.
- Call the small groups together after twenty minutes and invite each group to share with everyone what they have discovered.
- Write down some of these insights on the OHP or flip chart.

3. Mapping out your community

- Inform the group that what we understand by mapping a community is drawing up a description of our community which includes all the factors which have shaped it and how it operates on a spiritual and social level.
- Invite the people to divide up into small groups of four or five again, and ask them to go through the four areas in their group discussion.
- Bring them all together again after twenty minutes and invite them to share their findings.
- Write these up on an OHP or flip chart.
- Where there are differing opinions on the same subject, re-assure the people that we will have different perceptions depending upon our experience of the community, including whether we were born there or have only recently joined it.
- When this is done, if there is time, suggest a time of inter-cessory prayer on a representational model as preparation for the ministry time which is to follow.

4. Ministry to the community

This exercise may best be done on a separate occasion as it will require some quality time and must not be rushed.

Spend some time dividing the people up into small groups of threes or fours before going out into the community.

The purpose of this walk is to pray and to listen. As people walk around their community, they should ask God to make them alert to any particular needs that they can pray for there and then. They will also want to be aware of anything for which they want to **celebrate** in their community, and anything for which they want to **confess.** They need to keep a note of both the points for celebration and confession

At the feedback session write down the essential findings on the OHP or flip chart, in particular points for celebration and confession.

Following this, you need to decide upon a follow-up policy to build upon the work already done. For example:

- prayers of repentance and apology in the areas of neglect in the community;
- a policy of involvement in urban renewal working alongside of other community workers;
- holding a healing service in a wounded place in the town/city/village;
- celebrating the Holy Communion in places which need healing;
- additional prayer walking;
- deciding on how the church needs to change its ways to reach the needs of its community more effectively.

5. Summary and close

Read out the material in the course notes and remind people again to read the notes of Session 7 before the meeting. There is a lot of material in the next session, so it will really help if they can read the notes carefully before the meeting. The next meeting will be your last unless you have arranged further meetings. If it is the last, give thought on what might be an appropriate closure for your group.

Session 7:

TRIBAL AND NATION GROUP STORY

Course Notes

> *Outline for the session*
> 1. Healing the nations
> 2. Understanding my tribal story (group work)
> 3. Praying for the nation (group work)
> 4. Summary and close

1. HEALING THE NATIONS

We live in a time when the issues of nationhood and tribalism have assumed global importance. We have witnessed how the former state of Yugoslavia has disintegrated in a form of tribal warfare. Neighbours who had lived in relative peace with each other, almost overnight rose up in armed warfare with each other as people identified with their tribal groups based on religion and race, each with its own history and its old scores to settle. Consider how the age-long hatred between Kosovan Serb and Muslim erupted into a war of extermination. This has also been starkly displayed in Rwanda where the two major tribes of Hutu and Tutsi have been embroiled in a genocidal war. The Palestinian now has a homeland, but it is set in the context of an uneasy peace with its long-term tribal enemy, Israel. Australians want to remove what they call the outdated allegiance to the English monarchy, which is viewed as the last vestige of an intrusion of one nation upon another.

There has been a resurgence of reviving the culture and spirituality of the indigenous tribes of the North American Indians, the Amerindians, the Inuit and the aboriginal peoples of Australia and New Zealand. The Rainbow Nation of South Africa is seeking to come to terms with its violent history through the medium of the Truth and Reconciliation Committee. In the United Kingdom, issues of national identity have been revived with the move towards devolution for Scotland and Wales with their separate Parliament and Assembly. This issue of tribalism and national identity is nowhere more apparent than in the ongoing struggles in Northern Ireland, where the Protestant community traces its roots to the planting of Scottish immigrants in the seventeenth century and the Catholic Republicans regard themselves as the true people of the land. This historic antagonism is replayed every year with the Orange marches through Catholic housing estates.

All these people stories indicate that at some level it is important for us as individuals to recognise that we belong to a tribal or nation group which still has some influence over our lives. It is important therefore that as Christians we learn such stories and find appropriate processes for healing of such tribal and nation stories in order that the witness of the church may be effective within our societies. William Storrar in his book *Scottish Identity* says 'the church is the new acoustic community of all nations.'[1] He means that as a community of faith, the church should be aware of its nation's group story and find ways of bringing healing and renewal to that story, and not be a victim or repeater of it in its own life. After all, we as Christians have a God-given mandate to be part of the process which the Bible calls the healing of the nations. In the last reference to healing in scripture in Revelation 22:2 there is described, in idealised form, the city of the redeemed, which has mystical trees, the leaves of which are for the healing of the nations.

The Bible and the healing of the nations

The following is an outline of the story of care for the nations in Scripture:

(a) The covenant of the blessing of the nations

From the beginning God intended that his blessing be distributed to nations. When Abram is first called by God to leave his own tribal lands and become a pilgrim of faith, the covenant established with him stated 'and all the peoples on earth will be blessed through you' (Gen. 12:3). This theme is repeated and developed with each renewal of the covenant:

- Genesis 17:1–8: Abraham to become father of many nations;
- Genesis 17:16: Sarah to become mother of many nations;
- Genesis 18:18: Abraham to become a great and powerful nation and all nations on earth will be blessed through him.

Paul picks up these themes in his letter to the Galatian church when he writes that as believers of whatever gender, race or nationality, we are all one community in Christ (3:8–14; 26–9).

We can conclude from these references that the people of God are exhorted to live in such a way that their lives become a blessing to the other nations. It is a call to global stewardship.

(b) Israel and the nations

Among other things, this nation called by God is charged with the tasks of being a **model**, a **witness**, a **proclaimer** and a **pray-er** for the healing of the nations.

(i) A model of godly shared living

'Now if you obey me fully and keep my covenant, then out of all nations you will be my treasured possession. Although the whole earth is mine, you will be for me a kingdom of priests and a holy nation.'

(Exod. 19:5–6 NIV; cf. also Lev. 20:26; Deut. 10:15)

The ministry of the nation's priesthood is that of caring for all the nation's welfare and it is this faithful work which contributes to Israel's wholeness and holiness.

(ii) A witness to God's providence and care

- Deuteronomy 4:5–8: the keeping of God's laws and statutes serves as a witness to other nations of the value and attraction of wise and righteous living.
- 1 Kings 4:31 and 34: the wise rule of Solomon attracts the interest of surrounding nations.
- Isaiah 2:2: on the day of God's appearing the nations will come to the mount of God (cf. Jer. 3:17).

(iii) Proclaimer of God's word

Give thanks to the Lord, call on his name, make known among the nations what he has done. (1 Chron. 16:8 NIV)

Declare his glory among the nations. (1 Chron. 16:24 NIV)

He [the Messiah] will sprinkle many nations. (Isa. 52:15 NIV)

(iv) A pray-er for the healing of the nations

My house will be called a house of prayer for all the nations. (Isa. 56:7 NIV)

(c) Church and the nations

It is important to note before proceeding with this section that we cannot too easily make an identification of the church with the nation of Israel. Some say that the role of Israel is a unique example which cannot be transferred wholesale to the church. After all, the Scriptures do not explicitly say that the church is replacing Israel and becoming the new Israel. However, what is remarkable is that the mandate for Israel is the same as that for the church. Though different, Israel and the church of Jesus have the same calling as far as being a witness to the nations, and we need to take this seriously.

- With this in mind, what emerges from the New Testament are **parallel themes** for the church: The church is called to **model** a community life which is tantamount to being a holy nation and a royal priesthood for all (1 Pet. 2:9).
- With the coming of the Holy Spirit to this new community its first priority is to be a **witness** to the quality and value of the Lordship of Christ (Acts 1:8).
- The mandate given by Jesus to the Christian community he has called into being is to be a **proclaimer** of the good news of God's love and forgiveness to individuals and communities. In order to accomplish this it has to go into the whole world, and it is no surprise therefore that the first missionaries sought to reach the nation's conscience by focusing its centre of operations in the major cities of their day (Matt. 24:14; Luke 24:47).
- Finally, there is the classic reminder by Jesus that the church is also to be the vehicle of **prayer** for the healing of the nations. He entered the court of the Gentiles outside the Temple in Jerusalem and emptied it of the greedy moneychangers. He challenged them to remember that the focus of the Temple's ministry was not to extort the Gentiles and thereby wound their consciences but to be a prayer resource for their healing (Mark. 11:15–17).

UNDERSTANDING MY TRIBAL STORY (GROUP WORK)

> *History, despite its wrenching pain,*
> *Cannot be unlived,*
> *but if faced with courage,*
> *need not be lived again.* [2]

Another strand of our individuality is the fact that we carry, to a greater or lesser degree, a tribal or national group story as part of our make-up. Charles Elliot in his book *Memory and Salvation* introduces the question: who shapes whom? Do we shape society or does society shape us? I suspect that it is a bit of both. However, for our own growth into wholeness and for our ability to contribute to the healing of our tribal or national story, we may need to discover what that story is and how it continues to shape us today.

Example from Wales

At a conference for church leaders an incumbent of the Church in Wales first contributed to the discussion by saying that he had nothing against the English – he was happily married to an Englishwoman, after all! However, during a time of listening to God in order to hear something of the tribal story that might affect him, he realised that he did harbour feelings of resentment about the number of English ministers in his country. In his prayer for his people he said, 'Lord, please forgive us Welsh people for resisting the spread of the Gospel from the English because they stole our land and robbed us of our language.' He was referring to the historic battles between the English and the Welsh and to the fact that the English government did ban the speaking of Welsh in schools well into the twentieth century. He had realised that he carried something of his nation's memory, and that it did shape his actions to some degree.

Group work

You will be asked to form groups of about four. At the start you will need to establish what 'tribe' or 'nation' your small group wishes to identify with. You may wish to choose a regional group (e.g. Yorkshire, Cornwall, Welsh-speaking Welsh etc.), or you may wish to identify with your nation – England, Scotland, Wales, Ireland, or the UK etc., or your nation of origin (e.g. India, China, etc.).

You now have about 45 minutes to explore the following three main questions. We suggest you give about 15 minutes to each section. The questions will help you to discover something of your tribal or nation group story.

(a) What are your roots?

- What are the main features of the story?
- What is there to celebrate and confess?
- What are its relationships with other nations/tribes?

(b) Are there any noticeable patterns that recur?

You may find it useful to use the following four levels of listening to help you determine your answer:

 (i) **open**: that part of the story which is known and obvious;
 (ii) **hidden**: that part of the story which is underneath the surface;
 (iii) **denied**: that part of the story which is never owned or accepted;
 (iv) **unknown**: that part of the story which is new to you.

NB. As an example these questions were put to a small group representing different religious groups in the Republic of Ireland and Northern Ireland. The issue being investigated was the fears and suspicions felt by the Northern Ireland Protestant. The following is a brief and generalised summary of what was shared:

 (i) **open**: a mistrust of the intentions of the Catholic Republic;
 (ii) **hidden**: the fear that what has happened to the Southern Ireland Protestant will happen to them (i.e. loss of status and power);
 (iii) **denied**: that the Catholic in the North has a genuine grievance;
 (iv) **unknown**: an insecurity about their ancestor's role in securing their power base.

(c) How do these patterns affect your personal life?

Think about how the pattern in the nation/tribe actually affects your way of thinking.

 (i) What does this tell you about your self-identity?
 (ii) How does it affect the way you view others outside your group?

(iii) How do you feel when your group is hurting?

(iv) How do you feel when your group is responsible for hurting others either in the present or the past?

3. PRAYING FOR THE NATION (GROUP WORK)

> Asked if whether it was international sanctions which had brought about the end of apartheid, President De Klerk replied, 'It was not the sanctions, but a deep self analysis on our knees before God.'[3]

We have learnt that part of the ministry of the church is to pray for the healing of the nations. In this time of prayer we will use the material we have gathered about our tribal or nation group story.

Preparations for prayer

(a) Learning the power of apology

(b) Understanding social structures

(c) Acts of Jubilee

In the following group activity we will use these three sections, each of which includes a short time for reflection and discussion, followed by a prayer focus.

(a) Learning the power of apology

We live in a time where apology and reconciliation are important agendas for world political leaders who seek to improve the relationships between their country and another. At the time of the 150th commemoration of the tragedy of the Irish famine, Tony Blair, the British Prime Minister, apologised for his country's role in that disaster. John Bruton, the Irish Premier at the time, said, 'While the statement confronts the past honestly, it does so in a way that heals for the future.'

Consider also the example of John Presdee and the

Reconciliation Walks Prayer Expeditions. He felt convinced that one of the routes for healing relationships between Christians, Muslims and Jews was to apologise for the way the armies of the Western powers, in the name of Christ, had invaded their lands through the Crusades. Such actions had sown bitter resentment towards Christianity and led to a distorted view of the Christian faith. Consequently, on the 900th anniversary of the First Crusade, he walked the crusade route and visited mosques and synagogues to read out his apology. The following is his apology to Muslims:

> Nine hundred years ago, our forefathers carried the name of Jesus Christ to battle across Europe and the Middle East. Fuelled by fear, greed and hatred, they betrayed the name of Christ by conducting themselves in a manner contrary to his wishes and character. The Crusaders lifted the banner of the cross above your people, by this act they corrupted the meaning of reconciliation, forgiveness and selfless love.

> On the anniversary of the First Crusade, we also carry the name of Christ. We wish to retrace the footsteps of the Crusaders in apology for their deeds and in demonstration of the true meaning of the Cross. We deeply regret the atrocities committed in the name of Christ by our predecessors. We renounce greed, hatred and fear and condemn all violence done in the name of Jesus Christ. Jesus, the Messiah, came to bring life, forgive us for allowing his name to be associated with death. Please accept again the true meaning of the Messiah's words: *The Spirit of the Lord is upon me, because he has anointed me to bring good news to the poor. He has sent me to proclaim release to the captives and recovery of sight to the blind; to let the oppressed go free; to proclaim the year of the Lord's favour.*

The result has been a real interest on the part of his Muslim audiences throughout the walk to learn more about Jesus and the beginnings of a better awareness for healing between the communities. Apology creates a climate for listening to each other's wounded story and opens the possibility of healing wounded history and bringing better harmony between the nations.

In your group, consider:

1. Is there some part of your tribal story that needs confessing in apology?
2. Is there an appropriate action of apology you need to share with another tribal or nation group?

Focus for prayer

Using the form of representational confession, make this the focus of your prayer.

(b) Understanding social structures

Each tribe or nation has its institutions, ideas and rituals for maintaining its collective story and self-image. In your group, consider:

1. What are the main institutions that shape your tribe or nation?
2. Can you identify its 'spirit' or the ethos it gives out?
3. Can you identify the main 'rituals' for reinforcing your tribal story?

Focus for prayer

- Give thanks for what is good and needs to be blessed.
- Pray for ways to improve and change for the better.
- Pray for the healing of wounded memories.
- Pray for wisdom for the church to engage in activities that will enrich and heal the image of wholeness in the tribe or nation.

(c) Acts of Jubilee

At the heart of the Old Testament concept of Jubilee was the will to restore land to the kinship group to whom it originally belonged in the event of there being no available redeemer within the family. It was essentially a reflection on the need to belong on the land that was gifted to that family group. It was an act of healing and restoration. By the spirit of Jubilee, therefore, we are called to focus our attention on wounded land and the history of the peoples or group connected with it.

In your group, consider: can you identify particular *places* that contain the wounded history of your tribe/nation?

Focus for prayer
Pray as a group for the healing of such places.

As you end this prayer time, you may like to consider praying on the site itself. Make sure that in such prayers you include some symbolic way of remembering and respecting the peoples connected with the site.

4. SUMMARY AND CLOSE

(a) We have examined how tribal or nation group story has a role in our individual lives.
(b) Together we have prayed into some of the important features of our tribal or nation group story.

As we come to the end of this course, are there:

(a) ways in which we can follow through and build upon what we have learnt?
(b) programmes of involvement in our nation's story, environment and social ethos that we as a church can undertake?

Notes
1 William Storrar, *Scottish Identity* (Handsel Press, 1990), p. 118.
2 Maya Angelou, 'On the pulse of the morning', a poem for the inauguration of the President of the United States (New York: Random House, 1993).
3 Quoted in Nicholas Frayling, *Pardon and Peace* (London: SPCK, 1996), p. 110.

Further reading
Healing Wounded History, Chapter 12: 'The Tribal or Group Nation Story'.

Leader's Notes

1. Healing the nations

There is a lot of teaching in this section, so check that people have had a chance to read through the notes before the meeting. For a more thorough study of this section, you could cover the material in two meetings.

In the opening section, we hear about many different tribal and national groups – the various groups of Yugoslavia, Rwanda, the Middle East, Australia, North America, Australasia, South Africa and our own lands of Britain and Ireland.

After looking through this page, ask the group whether they have witnessed the effects of tribal and national conflict in this country or others they have visited.

The Bible and the healing of the nations

There are many Bible verses in this section. Hopefully people will have read a number of these before the meeting. You might like to pick out a few of the key verses.

With reference to the verses in Genesis about Abraham, ask: 'How do we live in such a way that our lives can be a blessing to other nations?'

In the section on Israel and the nations, try not to get distracted on issues to do with Israel, and keep the discussion focused on the healing of tribal and nation group story. Spend a bit of time in discussion about the parallel themes for the church. You may like to use the following questions:

- How can our church **model** a community life that lives out 1 Peter 2:9?
- How does the Holy Spirit help us, as a community group, to **witness** to Christ?

- How do we become **proclaimers** of the good news of God's love to our community?

We shall pick up **prayer** in the group work to follow.

2. Understanding my tribal story (group work)

Explain to the group that in the following group activity we shall be exploring our tribal or nation group story. Form people into groups of about four and ask them to turn to 'Understanding my tribal story: group work', and in particular to the group instructions and questions. Invite them to read these through and see if they need to clarify anything. Allow about 45 minutes for this discussion, i.e. 15 minutes for each section.

At the end of 45 minutes, ask people to finish their discussion work, and explain that we are now about to engage in the next group activity.

3. Praying for the nation (group work)

Explain that in a moment people will pray together in their groups for the tribe or nation with which they have identified. Their notes will guide them through the three sections for prayer:

(a) Learning the power of apology
(b) Understanding social structures
(c) Acts of Jubilee

Each section allows for a short discussion to help identify the focus for prayer. Encourage them to allow plenty of time for prayer and not to spend the whole time chatting! They will have 15 minutes for each section.

At the end of the 45 minutes, call the group whole group back together.

4. Summary and close

- Check out how the group found the prayer exercise.
- Check if, following the last section, they feel any place should be visited for prayer.

- Use the final two questions in the notes to see if any further action should be taken following this session's work.
- This is the last group meeting, so close it in the way you feel is appropriate.

Books Related to
Healing Wounded History

General

Brueggemann, Walter, *The Land*, SPCK, 1978.

Clinebell, Howard, *Ecotherapy*, Haworth Press, 1996.

Dawson, John, *Healing America's Wounds*, Regal Books, 1994.

Elliott, Charles, *Memory and Salvation*, DLT, 1995.

Falconer, Alan D. (ed.) *Reconciling Memories*, Columba Press, 1988.

Graham, Larry Kent, *Care of Persons, Care of Worlds*, Abingdon, 1992.

Kaminsky, Joel, *Corporate Responsibility in the Bible*, Sheffield Academic Press, 1995.

Linthicum, Robert, *City of God, City of Satan*, Zondervan, 1991.

Murray, Stuart, *The Challenge of the City*, Sovereign World, 1993.

Parker, Russ, *The Wild Spirit*, SPCK, 1997.

Parker, Russ, *Forgiveness is Healing*, DLT, 1993.

Books relating to specific sessions
Session 1: Healing Wounded Memories

Brueggemann, Walter, *The Land*, SPCK, 1978.

Dawson, John, *Healing America's Wounds*, Regal Books, 1994.

Elliott, Charles, *Memory and Salvation*, DLT, 1995.

Elson, Ron, *Green House Theology*, Monarch, 1992.

Kaminsky, Joel, *Corporate Responsibility in the Bible*, Sheffield Academic Press, 1995.

Pratney, Winkey, *Healing the Land*, Chosen Books, 1993.

Silvoso, Ed, *That None Should Perish*, Regal Books, 1986.

Wink, Walter, *Unmasking the Powers*, Fortress Press, 1986.

Session 2: Representational Confession

Coggan, Donald, *The Servant-Son*, Triangle, 1995.

Dawson, John, *What Christians Should Know about Reconciliation*, Sovereign World, 1998.

Goll, Jim, *Father Forgive Us*, Destiny Image, 1999.
Hauerwas, Stanley, *A Time to Heal*, ECONI, 1999.
Schreiter, Robert, *Reconciliation*, Orbis Books, 1992.

Session 3: Family Group Story
Carder, Dave, Henslin, Earl, Townsend, John and Cloud, Henry, *Secrets of Your Family Tree*, Moody Press, Chicago, 1991.
Mitton, Michael and Parker, Russ, *Requiem Healing*, Eagle Publications, 2001.
Wrigley, Dennis, *What on Earth Are We Doing to Our Children?*, Maranatha Community, 1995.

Session 4: Church Group Story
Brown, Wallace and Mary, *Angels on the Walls*, Kingsway, 2000.
Thwaites, Jim, *The Church Beyond the Congregation*, Paternoster Press, 1999.

Session 5: The Christian Day of Atonement
Parker, Russ, *Forgiveness is Healing*, DLT, 1993.

Session 6: Community Group Story
Bakke, Ray, *A Theology as Big as the City*, Monarch, 1997.
Linthicum, Robert, *City of God, City of Satan*, Zondervan, 1991.
Murray, Stuart, *The Challenge of the City*, Sovereign World, 1993.
Otis Jr, George, *The Last of the Giants*, Chosen Books, 1991.
Parker, Russ, *The Wild Spirit*, SPCK, 1997.
Parker, Russ and Lawrence, Roy, *Healing and Evangelism*, Triangle, 1996.

Session 7: Tribal and Nation Group Story
Sandford, John Loren, *Healing the Nations*, Monarch, 2000.

Liturgical Resources
Owens, Jimmy and Carol, *Heal Our Land; Praise and Prayer to Change a Nation*. Introduction packet obtainable from:

P O Box 75189
Colorado Springs
CO 80970
USA

Fax: 716 632 2500
Email: healourland@compuserve.com